The WILD Thornberrys ™

Joke Book

**KLASKY
CSUPO**INC.

Based on the TV series *The Wild Thornberrys*® created by Klasky Csupo, Inc.,
as seen on Nickelodeon®

ISBN 0-439-28334-5

12 11 10 9 8 7 6 5 4 3 2 1   1 2 3 4 5 6/0

Printed in the U.S.A.
First Scholastic printing, May 2001

The WILD Thornberrys™

Joke Book

FUNNY ANIMAL JOKES

BY DAVID LEWMAN

SCHOLASTIC INC.

New York Toronto London Auckland Sydney
Mexico City New Delhi Hong Kong

NICKELODEON®

Nigel: What do you get when you cross Eliza with a reptile?

Debbie: Elizard!

Marianne: What do you get when you cross Eliza with a bird?

Debbie: Owliza!

Nigel: What do you get when you cross Eliza with a fish?

Debbie: Eeliza!

Debbie: What do you call your best friend when he beats you at a game?

Eliza: Darwinner!

Are the Thornberrys smart?

Yes, they're very sharp.

Eliza: Why is Mom filming that native bread?

Nigel: She needs some wild-loaf footage.

Marianne: How does Donnie like traveling with us?

Eliza: He's wild about it.

Darwin: What kind of insect has long blonde hair and reads *Teenage Wasteland?*

Eliza: A Deb-bee.

Eliza: What has red hair and goes great on toast?

Darwin: Nigelly!

Eliza: What do you get when you cross my mom with a tiny insect?

Darwin: A Mari-ant.

Eliza: What do you get when you cross Donnie with an old elephant?

Debbie: A mastodonnie.

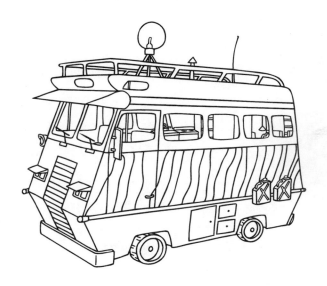

Eliza: What do you call our camper when it turns too fast?

Darwin: The Commveer.

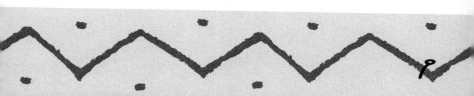

Eliza: Knock, knock.

Darwin: Who's there?

Eliza: Skip.

Darwin: Skip who?

Eliza: 'S Kip O'Donnell—run!

Marianne: What did Nigel say when the elephant stepped on the coconut?

Debbie: "Smashing!"

Debbie: What would you call Kip's sidekick if he were a bug?

Eliza: Beetleman.

Darwin: What would you sing if you saw Biederman's partner raising animals in the country?

Eliza: "Kip O'Donnell had a farm, E, I, E, I, O . . ."

Darwin: Why is Nigel so interested in wildlife?

Eliza: It's just his nature.

Eliza: Why did Donnie push Mom's film equipment down the mountain?

Nigel: He wanted to roll the cameras.

Eliza: What did the film say to the camera?

Darwin: "Look at me—I'm on a roll!"

Darwin: What's Nigel's favorite constellation?

Eliza: The Big Kipper.

Nigel: Knock, knock.

Debbie: Who's there?

Nigel: Saul.

Debbie: Saul who?

Nigel: Salty kippers—yum!

Darwin: How long has Donnie been wild?

Eliza: Since the day he was Borneo.

Eliza: What'll happen to Darwin if he eats too many of his favorite treats?

Nigel: He'll turn into a chimpancheesy.

Nigel: How did Eliza feel after eating too much of her favorite pudding?

Marianne: Plum tuckered out.

What did Eliza sing when she heard something ringing in the Amazon?

"Jungle bells, jungle bells, jungle all the way..."

How have the Thornberrys' trips to Africa gone?

Safari, so good.

Debbie: Who sells the wettest flowers in South America?

Marianne: The rain florist.

Eliza: Which woods are the smartest?

Darwin: The brain forest.

Eliza: Which woods are full of kings and queens?

Darwin: The reign forest.

Marianne: What happened when the boy volcano met the girl volcano?

Debbie: It was lava at first sight.

Do Darwin and Eliza like to go up trees together?

Yes, they're partners-in-climb.

What did Debbie say when Darwin fell out of the tree?

"Better luck next climb."

What do you call Eliza, Darwin, and Donnie when they climb trees together?

The Tree Musketeers.

Eliza: Which tree has the best food in it?

Darwin: The pantry.

Eliza: Which tree always stays warm?

Darwin: The fir tree.

Eliza: Which tree is always handy?

Darwin: The palm.

Can Eliza talk to trees?

No, but she understands their bark.

Eliza: Why aren't trees good actors?

Nigel: They give wooden performances.

Eliza: Can you ride on a vine, Darwin?

Darwin: Yes, I think I can swing it.

Why did Eliza and Darwin climb on vines?

They wanted to be in the swing of things.

23

Is Darwin like his father?

Yes, he's a chimp off the old block.

What do you call Darwin covered in black and white stripes?

A chimpanzebra.

What do you call Darwin when he's eaten way too much?

A blimpanzee.

Eliza: Who's big, green, and hangs around in the jungle?

Debbie: Frankenvine.

Which ape is the smallest?

The shrimpanzee.

Eliza: Knock, knock.

Debbie: Who's there?

Eliza: Annie.

Debbie: Annie who?

Eliza: Animals are my life!

Debbie: Where do creatures go shopping?

Nigel: The ani-mall.

Debbie: Knock, knock.

Eliza: Who's there?

Debbie: School.

Eliza: School who?

Debbie: 'S cool to be me, you know?

Debbie: How do you like my jeans, Dad?

Nigel: I think they're ripping!

What does Nigel call it
when his daughters
perform?

A poppet show.

Why are moutains
smelly?

They're right next
to the foothills.

What does Eliza say to
a cat when she's hurt
herself?

"Me-ow!"

How did Eliza do when she tried to talk to mice?

She squeaked by.

Why did Eliza read a whole book to the warthog?

She wanted to make a long story snort.

Why didn't Eliza tell the wild boar her secrets?

She was afraid he'd squeal.

Did the wild boar have a stand-in for the Thornberrys' nature film?

No, he did all his own grunts.

Darwin: Why did Donnie race to the top of the tree?

Eliza: He wanted to be a runner-up.

What do you get when you cross a crocodile and a parrot?

A squawkodile.

Nigel: Why did Eliza put Donnie on her shoulders?

Marianne: She wanted to wear a jumper.

Nigel: Why does Donnie run in bed?

Marianne: Because he's fast asleep.

What did Debbie say when Eliza told her she saw a warthog in the forest?

"Wartever!"

What is Debbie's favorite fruit?

BOYSenberries.

Why did Debbie come to a screeching halt?

She saw a shop sign.

Eliza: What do you call a shopping center in the jungle?

Debbie: The Mall of the Wild.

What does Debbie call it when Eliza dances with Darwin?

"Dancing geek-to-geek."

What happened to Biederman's plan to set a trap with a covered pit?

It fell through.

Why did Eliza say "excuse me" to the bird?

She chirped.

Why didn't Eliza talk to the mountain goat behind the shrub?

She didn't want to bleat around the bush.

What did Eliza ask the wild donkey's mother?

"Can your daughter come out and bray?"

What did the horse tell Eliza after the race?

"You whinny some, you losey some."

What did Eliza say to the horse?

"That's easy for you to neigh."

Darwin: What do you call a horse who's dull to talk to?

Eliza: A neigh-bore.

Darwin: Why are wolf sentences so hard to untangle?

Eliza: They're always snarled.

What do you call a cat who speaks like a parakeet?

A cheeping tom.

What do you call a parakeet who dresses up like a dog?

A cheep in wolf's clothing.

Why couldn't Eliza understand the duck?

He had a very strong quackcent.

Darwin: What do you call the geese's leader?

Eliza: A honker chief.

What did the frog say when he heard Eliza talk?

"The croak's on you."

How does Eliza talk to crows?

Cawtiously.

What's it called when a crow makes a joke?

Cawmedy.

What were Eliza and the owl talking about?

They were just hooting the breeze.

Darwin: Does that pigeon know how he lost his voice?

Eliza: He doesn't have a coo.

How was the Thornberrys' show about desert animals?

A little dry.

Darwin: What position did the crab play on the baseball team?

Eliza: Pinch critter.

Eliza: Why do desert animals always brag?

Darwin: They're full of hot air.

What did Eliza say after she saw an avalanche?

"That rocked!"

Why did Marianne shoot the film during a sandstorm?

She'd been saving it for a grainy day.

Debbie: What's the smelliest part of a movie?

Marianne: The footage.

Why did Nigel and Marianne film the biggest animal at the end of the day?

They saved the beast for last.